Once Upon a Memory

Reflections of Childhood

Copyright © 1995

Brownlow Publishing Company

6309 Airport Freeway

Fort Worth, Texas 76117

ISBN: 1-57051-042-3

Cover/Interior:

Koechel Peterson & Associates

Printed in the USA

A SPECIAL GIFT

For:

Heather D. Fellows
From:

Rex & Jana Kindall

With Love!

Date

12-25-96

Cherished Moments
Gift Books

Merry Christmas With Love

Once Upon a Memory
Reflections of Childhood

Sweet Rose of Friendship

Tea for Two
Taking Time for Friends

Once Upon a Memory

Reflections of Childhood

LITTLE MABEL

All day long my little Mabel
Worked as hard as she was able,
Chasing butterflies and bees,
Underneath the apple trees;
Stringing daisies in a chain
For her dolly, Lady Jane.

Mabel was so very busy
That it made me almost dizzy
Just to watch her running over
All the meadow, red with clover,
Out into the shady lane
With her dolly, Lady Jane.

There, beneath the spreading boughs,
She has built her baby-house,—
Bits of china, blue and white,
Decked with buttercups so bright;
There at set of sun I found her,
With all her treasures around her.

But so tired my little lady,
In her nook so cool and shady,
That her dolly tightly clasping,
And a tiny tea-cup grasping,
Close beside her little table,
Fast asleep, sat darling Mabel!

Thou art the star that guides me
Along life's changing sea:
And whate'er fate betides me,
This heart still turns to thee.

George P. Morris

Playing School

Come, come, my dears, it's time for school,

So please sit down all in a row.

Laughing is quite against the rule;

I've told you that before, you know.

Now try to say your A B C

Together, slowly, after me.

LITTLE CAROLINE

Early to bed, early to rise,
Made little Caroline healthy and wise.

Up in the morning she rose with the sun
And did not play till her work was done.

Her happy face and her merry song
Made joy and sunshine the whole day long.

She helped her mother about the house,
And while baby slept was still as a mouse.

She studied her little books with care,
And learned the lessons set her there.

Of play she rarely had quite enough:
She loved it well, but never was rough.

Though poor herself to the poor she gave;
For some little money she often could save.

And so she was loved by great and small
Because she was kind and good to all.

Emily Carter

THE DAYS GONE BY

O the days gone by! O the days gone by!

The apples in the orchard,

and the pathway through the rye;

The chirrup of the robin, and the whistle of the quail

As he piped across the meadows

sweet as any nightingale;

When the bloom was on the clover,

and the blue was in the sky,

And my happy heart brimmed over

in the days gone by.

James Whitcomb Riley

POOR LITTLE MUGS

"Well, you poor little soul, I don't know what is to be done with you now your foolish mother has got killed in that rabbit-burrow," said Squire Stubbs, gazing down at a big-headed, soft-legged puppy, who gazed back at him with an equally mournful expression. "I just think we had better tie a stone round your neck, and put you in the pond."

"Oh, no, Father!" cried little Peggy, her eyes filling with tears. "Oh, don't! Give him to me, Father. I'll feed him and see after him; indeed I will."

So it was agreed that Peggy was to be a kind of little mother to Mugs (such was the puppy's name), but she soon found her post to be no easy task, for a more unfortunate puppy, or one more apt to get into mischief, never breathed. Even as he grew older he developed all sorts of vexatious ways. At last, after having nearly met his death in the preserves, and once tumbling through the thin ice of a pond and being rescued by Peggy, at the peril of her life and the ruin of her frock, and after every day chasing the young chickens, and dashing into the pond after the ducks, and doing every mortal thing a little dog ought not to do, he was condemned to exile. The shepherd was to take him to his cottage on the moor and see if he could mend his manners. Poor little Peggy wept bitter tears, for, with all his faults, she was devoted to Mugs, as Mugs was to her; but the Squire would not give way, and Mugs was led away, looking as miserable an animal as ever was seen.

But next morning there was a grand row in the farmyard, and lo! there was Mugs triumphant, with a broken bit of rope round his neck, chasing the ducks and chickens as cheerfully as ever. He had managed to break loose and find his way home.

But his joy was short-lived. Again he was captured, and again led off; and for some days there was peace in the poultry-yard.

It was night—a still, dark night. Everyone was asleep when suddenly everyone was awakened by a dreadful clamor below. Shouts, blows, barks, yells, then muffled growlings, and general turmoil, in the midst of which out rushed the Squire and his men in haste.

"What is this?" shouted the Squire. "Who is there?" But whoever was there did not wait to reply, for two figures were dimly seen jumping over the gate and fleeing away into the darkness.

"Thieves, as I'm alive!" shouted the old gentleman. "Mark! Harry! Follow them! Here, bring a light. What's this?" For he struck his foot against something soft, which gave a little moan. "It's a dog! It's Mugs!" he cried, as someone brought a candle, "and he's half-killed. What is that in his teeth?—a bit of twill cloth. Why, the little chap must have got loose again and caught the thieves here!"

"And not too soon," said old Tom. "They had got the door almost open, Squire; see, here's their tools, and he got one of 'em by the leg. Here, let me see what can be done. He's badly hurt!"

But though Mugs was half-killed, he was not wholly so, and with great care and nursing he recovered. It need scarcely be said that he was never sent away again, and, for the future, was allowed to bark at the ducks as much as he liked.

FRIENDS

Give me a few friends who will love me for what I am, or am not, and keep ever burning before my wondering steps the kindly light of hope. And though age and infirmity overtake me, and I come not in sight of the castle of my dreams, teach me still to be thankful for life and time's old memories that are good and sweet. And may the evening twilight find me gentle still.

Author Unknown

Children are the hands by which we

take hold of heaven.

Henry Ward Beecher

How great is the love the Father has lavished on us, that

we should be called children of God!

And that is what we are!

1 John 3:1

Children are messengers we send

to a time we will not see.

Scenes of Childhood

How dear to my heart

are the scenes of my childhood,

When fond recollection

presents them to view!

Samuel Woodworth

THE SCARECROW

Funny old scarecrow! you're still left there,

Though the seeds have grown up, and there's no one to scare.

We're not afraid of you, don't think that;

You're only Meg's shawl, and Daddy's old hat!

You've got two arms, but they're very thin;

And you've got no mouth to put toffee in;

And you've no hands to play with the snow.

I shouldn't like to be you, I know!

You're not afraid, Roger? Look and see;

He's not a live thing, like you and me.

He's only sticks, tied together with string.

I wouldn't be him for anything!

He never sleeps, and he never wakes,

Nor hears the noise that the church-bell makes.

He's never naughty, and never good.

I think he'd like to be us if he could!

Suppose he was us! Suppose he was me!

And had my clothes and went home to my tea!

And I was him, to stand out there,

All covered with ice, in the frosty air!

He can't feel the cold, and perhaps at night

He sees the fays in the bright moonlight!

But not even for that would I choose to be he;

For whatever there is, he's no eyes to see!

THINGS OF
DEAREST WORTH

These are the things I prize
And hold of dearest worth:
Light of the sapphire skies,
Peace of the silent hills,
Shelter of the forests, comfort of the grass,
Music of birds, murmurs of little rills,
Shadows of clouds that swiftly pass,
And, after showers,
The smell of flowers
And of the good brown earth,—
And best of all, along the way,
friendship and mirth.

Henry Van Dyke

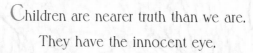

Children are nearer truth than we are.

They have the innocent eye.

Sir Hugh Casson

EVERYBODY SAYS

Everybody says
I look just like my mother.
Everybody says
I'm the image of Aunt Bee.
Everybody says
My nose is like my father's,
But I want to look like me.

Dorothy Aldis

SUNBEAMS

Sunbeams are the golden children

Of the great and mighty sun,

And he lets them come to see us,

Some in earnest, some for fun.

Then about the world they wander,

And they always try to find

How they may be good and useful,

How they may be sweet and kind.

But the sun is very careful
Lest they should take harm or cold;
So he bids them come home early,
And they do as they are told.

Then he counts them over slowly,
And the smallest child would miss.
Then he blesses them and gives
Each a rosy good-night kiss.

LITTLE
DROPS
OF WATER

Little drops of water,
Little grains of sand,
Make the mighty ocean
And the pleasant land.

Little deeds of kindness,
Little words of love,
Help to make earth happy
Like the heaven above.

The heart is happiest
when it beats for others.

AS A CHILD

As a little child relies
On a care beyond its own,
Knows beneath its father's eyes
It is never left alone,—

So let me, a child, receive
What today Thou shalt provide,
Calmly to Thy wisdom leave
What tomorrow may betide.

Quiet, Lord, my anxious heart,
Make me loving, meek and mild;
Upright, simple, free from art,
Keep me as a little child.

J. Newton

Love has hands to help others. It has feet to hasten to the poor and needy. It has eyes to see misery and want. It has ears to hear the sighs and sorrows of men. This is what love looks like.

Augustine

Nature gives
to every time
and season
some beauties
of its own.

Charles Dickens

OUT IN THE FIELDS

Bring the children to the fields,

Where the sheep are straying;

With the birds and butterflies,

Let them now be playing;

On the hill-side, in the glen,

All the green lawn over,

Through the yellow buttercups,

Down among the clover!

With the sunshine in their hearts,

In their cheeks the roses,

Let them breathe the balmy air,

Let them gather posies;

In this merry month of June,

Summer's fairest weather,

Let the children and the flowers

Bud and bloom together.

Anna Livingstone

THANK YOU, GOD

God made the little flowers bloom

And made each rustling tree;

He made each bird and blade of grass;

And then He thought of me.

Thank You, dear God, for making the flowers

And touching each rustling tree,

For making birds and a blade of grass;

And thank You for making me.

A Tea Party

You see, merry Phyllis, that dear little maid,

Has invited Belinda to tea;

Her nice little garden is shaded by trees,–

What pleasanter place could there be?

There's a cake full of plums, there are strawberries too,

And the table is set on the green;

I'm fond of a carpet all daisies and grass, –

Could a prettier picture be seen?

Kate Greenaway

A happy childhood is one of the best gifts
that parents have in their power to bestow.

R. Cholmondeley

RAIN

The rain is raining all around,

It falls on field and tree,

It rains on the umbrellas here,

And on the ships at sea.

Robert Louis Stevenson

THE LITTLE MONKEY

"Nursey," said Miss Lil one morning, "Father has given me a whole large penny." "Has he, Miss?" said Nurse. "Why do you suppose he did that?" "He gave it to me for my thoughts," answered Lil. "He said to me that morning, 'A penny for your thoughts, Lil.' It looks like a gold penny, doesn't it? And, now, what shall I buy with it, Nursey, dear?" "Well, what do you want most, Missy?"

"I might buy a little dolly for Miranda to play with," continued Lil. "Can I get a dolly for a penny, Nursey?" "Oh! yes, I think so," answered Nurse. "You can buy a little china or wooden dolly for a penny, I feel sure. When we were children we used to get little wooden dollies, two a penny. They were not so pretty as the dollies now, but they had jointed legs and arms, and you could make them sit down, and sometimes stand up. I hardly know whether you can buy that kind now."

"Would they really sit down?" cried Lil, a little excited, "because that is what Miranda won't do. She is so stiff in the middle. Then I might buy a chair. I saw some penny chairs in the shop yesterday, and the little dolly could sit in it."

"But if you buy the dolly, you won't have any penny left to buy the chair."

"Oh, dear!" Lil exclaimed, rather in dismay. Her face fell a little, for a beautiful vision of a jointed wooden doll sitting up in a chair was rising in her mind. "But, oh, Nursey, what is that funny noise?" and Lil started up and ran to the window.

"Oh! it is a little boy and he has a monkey—such a funny little monkey in a frock, with a cap on his head. And now he plays a tune, the monkey runs about and dances and bows. Oh! Nursey, let us go outside and see him; let's do, please."

Nurse put on Lil's sunbonnet, and then they went into the front garden. The little boy came just in at the gate and smiled at her with his soft dark eyes, and made his monkey go through all his tricks; but Lil was a tiny bit afraid of the little creature, and shrank back close to Nurse.

"Is he your monkey, your very own?" asked Lil.

"Yes, he is," said the lad.

"Then I expect you are kind to him," said Nurse, "and that's why he obeys you."

"I love Jocko," the boy answered simply, "and Jocko loves me."

"Nursey," whispered Lil, "my penny, may I give the monkey my penny?"

"Do, Miss, if you like," said Nurse. "I would give him one also, but I sent all my money away yesterday to Mother because Father is out of work." So Lil pulled out her bright penny and dropped it into Jocko's cap, and Jocko's master thanked her in soft words and smiles.

And Miss Lil was really happier in giving her penny to the poor little boy than if she had bought half-a-dozen jointed dollies and chairs for them to sit on. She would have been happier still if she could have known how her penny was spent—to buy nuts and oranges for the poor boy and his monkey.

TWO PENNIES

Here is a penny! Here's another,
In each little handy-pandy;
So let us stop, for here's the shop
Of dear old Mary Candy.
How much will two pennies purchase?
Let us reckon, you and I,
For we're going to have a picnic
In the meadows by and by.

There are cheesecakes by the dozen.
There are tarts and creams and ices,
And toffee-drops and lollipops,
And everything that nice is.
Oh! what will two pennies purchase?
Let's ask her, you and I,
For we're going to have a picnic
In the meadows by and by.

What we desire our children to become,
we must endeavor to be before them.

Andrew Combe

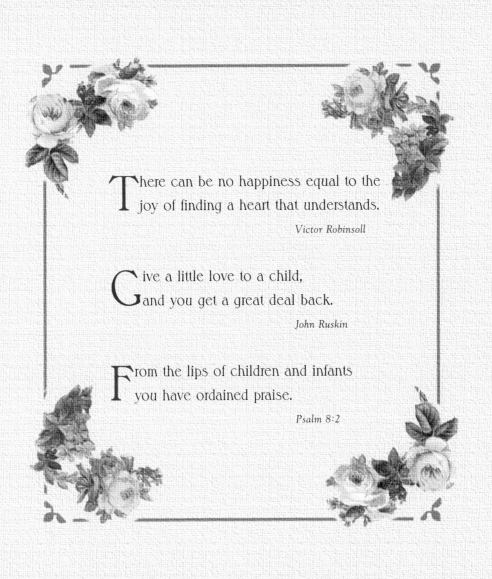

There can be no happiness equal to the joy of finding a heart that understands.

Victor Robinsoll

Give a little love to a child, and you get a great deal back.

John Ruskin

From the lips of children and infants you have ordained praise.

Psalm 8:2

LITTLE LAMB

Good morning to you, little lamb,
I want to kiss you so.
I love to see you frisk about;
I love your coat of snow.
See here! I've brought some flowers for you,
The best that I could find;
So kiss me, kiss me, little lamb,
And do not be unkind.

O little lamb! O little lamb!
How happy you should be
To live upon the pleasant grass
'Neath many a shady tree,

To crop away the grass all day
Amid the sunny hours,
While I must live in London town
And scarcely see the flowers.

I'd like to live like you all day
Amid the deep cool grass,
And see the humming-bees at play,
And hear the birdies pass.
But where I live the streets are hard,
The sky is never blue.
O little lamb! O little lamb!
I wish I were like you.

ONLY A BABY SMALL

Only a baby small,
Dropt from the skies;
Only a laughing face,
Two sunny eyes;

Only two cherry lips,
One chubby nose;
Only two little hands,
Ten little toes;

Only a golden head,
Curly and soft;
Only a tongue that wags
Loudly and oft;

Only a little brain,
Unvexed by thought;
Only a little heart,
Troubled with naught;

Only a tender flower,
Sent us to rear,
Only a life to love
While we are here.

ALL IS RIGHT

The year's at the spring

And day's at the morn;

Morning's at seven;

The hillside's dew-pearled;

The lark's on the wing;

The snail's on the thorn;

God's in His heaven—

All's right with the world.

Robert Browning

The fullness of life
does not come from the things outside us;
we ourselves must create the beauty
in which we live.

C. E. Cowman